W9-ACK-143

Text copyright © 1982 by Margaret Hillert. Illustrations and cover
design copyright © 1982 by Pearson Education, Inc., publishing as
Modern Curriculum Press, an imprint of Pearson Learning Group,
299 Jefferson Road, Parsippany, NJ 07054. Original illustrations
and cover design copyright © 1982 by Follett Publishing Company.
All rights reserved. No part of this book may be reproduced or
transmitted in any form or by any means, electronic, or mechanical,
including photocopying, recording, or by any information storage
and retrieval system, without permission in writing from the
publisher. For information regarding permission(s), write to Rights
and Permissions Department.

ISBN: 0-8136-5591-9
Printed in the United States of America

14 15 16 17 18 19   06 05 04 03 02

1-800-321-3106
www.pearsonlearning.com

TOM THUMB

Modern Curriculum Press
BEGINNING
TO
READ
Series

TOM THUMB

Margaret Hillert

Illustrated by Dennis Hockerman

We want a little boy.
Little boys are fun.
Where can we get
a little boy?

Oh, look here!
Look in here!
Here is a little boy.
A little, little boy.

6

Good, good.
This is what I want.
I like this little one.

7

Mother, Mother.
Look where I am.
Come and get me.
Help! Help!

8

9

Oh, my. Oh, my.
How did you get in here?
Come out. Come out.

And get in here.
Now see what you
have to do.

11

Come with me now.

We will go out here.

We will walk and walk.

Look here.

Here is something big.

12

Oh, oh.
Here I go.
In, in, in.
Help, Mother! Help!

13

Here you are.
You are out now.
You are here with me.

14

15

I am not with you now.
I am up here.
Up, up, up.

Now here I go down.

Down, down, down.

What can I do?

18

Oh, help! Help!
Something wants to eat me.
Here I go.

19

And here I am.
But what is this?
Where am I?

Oh, look. Look.
Here is a little, little
boy.
I want this boy.

22

Here is something for you.

Sit down on it.

Sit here with me.

I like you.

23

And I like to ride.
It is fun to ride.
Here is something for
you to ride, too.

25

This is fun.
I like to do this.
I like to ride and ride.

But I want to go away now.
I want to see my mother and
my father.

Here is something for you.
It is something good to have.
Take it with you.

Oh, this is good.
But it is so big.
It makes me work.
Work, work, work.

29

Here I am, Mother and Father.
Look what I have.
It is for you.
It will help you.

Margaret Hillert, author of several books in the MCP Beginning-To-Read Series, is a writer, poet, and teacher.

Tom Thumb uses the 60 words listed below.

a	father	makes	take
am	for	me	this
and	fun	mother	to
are		my	too
away	get		
	go	not	up
big	good	now	
boy(s)			walk
but	have	oh	want(s)
	help	on	we
can	here	one	what
come	how	out	where
			will
do	I	ride	with
did	in		work
down	is	see	
	it	sit	you
eat		so	
	like	something	
	little		
	look		